FOCUS

on Grammar and Punctuation

Grammar and Punctuation

Introductory Book

Louis Fidge

Collins

FOCUS
on Grammar
and Punctuation

Using this book

This book will help you to understand grammar and punctuation, and improve your writing. You will learn how sentences are structured and formed, how words work together and the rules of our language. Punctuation goes hand in hand with grammar – punctuation marks make writing easier to understand.

What's in a unit

Each unit is set out in the same way as the example here. There are also Progress Units to help you check how well you are doing.

Unit heading —
This tells you what you will be learning about

The rule
This explains the rule and gives an example

Making sure
Activities to practise and develop your understanding

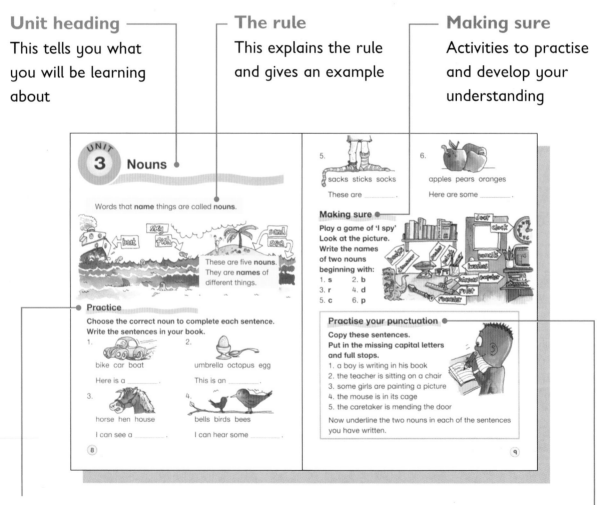

Practice
Activities to practise and check your understanding

Practise your punctuation —
Activities to practise and check your punctuation

Contents

Capital letters and full stops

Every **sentence** should begin with a **capital letter**. Most sentences end with a **full stop**.

Monkeys live in trees.

This sentence begins with a capital letter. It ends with a full stop.

Practice

Write these sentences correctly.

Put in the missing capital letters and full stops.

1. the farmer had some cows
2. clowns make us laugh
3. lemonade is fizzy
4. elephants have two tusks and a trunk
5. bluebells grow in the woods
6. children like to play marbles

Making sure

Write a sentence about each person. Say how they feel.
Use the words from the box to help you.
The first one has been done for you.

happy	sad	sleepy	surprised	frightened

girl   boy   baby

The girl is sad.

man   woman

Practise your punctuation

Copy this story. Put in all the missing capital letters and full stops.

two children went to the park
they took their dog
the dog chased some squirrels
the dog got lost
the children were worried
they did not know what to do

Write some more sentences to finish the story.

UNIT 2 Asking Questions

A **question** is a special kind of sentence. We ask **questions** to find out things.

Have you seen my skates?

A question begins with a **capital letter** and ends with a **question mark**.

Practice

Write these questions correctly. Put in the capital letters and question marks.

1. when is your birthday
2. where do you live
3. who is your teacher
4. what number comes before twenty
5. why do you go to school

Now write a sensible answer for each question.

Making sure

Write each question correctly.

1. what is Sam wearing
2. who is Sam with
3. where are the boys going
4. how did they get to the shop
5. what can they buy in the shop
6. when does the shop close

Use the picture to help you write an answer for each question.

Now make up two questions of your own about the picture.

Practise your punctuation

**Punctuate these sentences correctly.
Put in the capital letters, full stops and question marks.**

1. how many children are there in your class
2. who is your best friend
3. the toy shop was shut
4. is it raining today
5. some children keep pets at home
6. do you have a favourite sport

Words that **name** things are called **nouns**.

These are five **nouns**. They are **names** of different things.

Practice

Choose the correct noun to complete each sentence.
Write the sentences in your book.

1.

bike car boat

Here is a _____.

2.

umbrella octopus egg

This is an _____.

3.

horse hen house

I can see a _____.

4.

bells birds bees

I can hear some _____.

5.

sacks sticks socks

These are _____.

6.

apples pears oranges

Here are some _____.

Making sure

Play a game of 'I spy'
Look at the picture.
Write the names
of two nouns
beginning with:

1. **s**   2. **b**
3. **r**   4. **d**
5. **c**   6. **p**

Practise your punctuation

**Copy these sentences.
Put in the missing capital letters
and full stops.**

1. a boy is writing in his book
2. the teacher is sitting on a chair
3. some girls are painting a picture
4. the mouse is in its cage
5. the caretaker is mending the door

Now underline the two nouns in each of the sentences
you have written.

Proper Nouns

Names of people are a special kind of noun.
They are called **proper nouns**.
Proper nouns always begin with a **capital letter**.

My name is Jack.

I'm Jill.

Jack and Jill

Practice

Write the names of these characters from famous stories. Begin each with a capital letter.

cinderella

goldilocks

paddington bear

little boy blue

red riding hood

jack

Making sure

> The names of the days and months are also proper nouns. They begin with capital letters.

1. Write the names of the days correctly.
   Put them in the right order.
   monday   thursday   saturday
   wednesday   sunday   friday   tuesday

> Here are the names of the first six months of the year.

2. Write the names of these months in the correct order.
   March   June   January   April   February   May

3. Now write the names of the last six months of the year in the correct order.

Practise your punctuation

Punctuate these sentences correctly.

1. edward likes wednesday best because he has art
2. emma had her birthday in july
3. does march come before october
4. shanaz lives in brendon avenue
5. is france bigger than germany
6. mr and mrs grant went to spain on holiday in july

UNIT 5 Verbs

Doing words are called **verbs.**

The tiger **hides** in the bushes.

Verbs tell us what someone or something is **doing**.

Practice

Write a sentence and say what the children are doing in each picture.

Use the verbs from the box to help.

eating jumping flying sleeping crying reading

Do it like this: 1. The boy is reading.

1.

2.

3.

4.

5.

6.

Making sure

Match up the nouns with the verbs to say how different animals move.

Do it like this: Fish swim.

Nouns	Verbs
1. Fish	slither.
2. Birds	scamper.
3. Snakes	gallop.
4. Snails	swim.
5. Mice	prowl.
6. Elephants	slide.
7. Horses	fly.
8. Lions	lumber.

Practise your punctuation

Write these sentences correctly.

1. the frog splashed in the pond
2 you cut paper with scissors
3. karen and raza watched television
4. gary gold plays his guitar well
5. mrs green walked to the shops
6. mr burton hums while he peels the potatoes

Now underline the verbs in the sentences you have written.

Joining Sentences

We can join two short sentences together to make one longer sentence.

Jack went to the market. + He sold his cow.
Jack went to the market **and** sold his cow.

The two sentences have been joined with **and**.

Practice

Make these two sentences into one sentence using *and*. The first one has been done for you.

1. I went to the park. I saw my friend.

   I went to the park and saw my friend.

2. Tess brushed her teeth. She went to bed.

3. Humpty Dumpty sat on the wall. He had a great fall.

4. Sarah has fair hair. She has blue eyes.

5. Mr Smart opened the shed. He got out his garden fork.

6. The dog barked. It chased the burglar.

Making sure

Copy these sentences. Underline the joining word in each. The first one has been done to help you.

1. The door is shut <u>but</u> the window is open.

2. The road was busy and crowded with cars.

3. Ben ate some chocolate before he went home for lunch.

4. It rained while we were in school.

5. The mouse saw the cat then ran under the chair.

6. The sun shone brightly until it was time to go home.

Practise your punctuation

Write your own ending for each sentence.

1. Kate likes swimming but _____ .

2. Nadeem went to the shop and _____ .

3. The squirrel ran up the tree and _____ .

4. The kangaroo hopped until _____ .

5. Shireen fell over after _____ .

Writing Sentences

A **sentence** is a group of words that makes **sense**. The words must be in the **correct order**.

The girl a book is reading.

↑

This sentence does not make sense. Some words are in the wrong order.

The girl is reading a book.

↑

This sentence makes sense. The words are in the **correct order**.

Practice

Write these sentences so they make sense.

1. Dogs bark can.
2. Fish live water in.
3. My cat milk likes.
4. The horse fast runs.
5. A kangaroo hopping likes.

Making sure

These sentences do not make sense.
Rewrite them correctly.

1. The postman bit the dog.
2. The football kicked the boy.
3. A blue dress wore the girl.
4. The ladder fell off the builder.
5. A guitar was playing the pop singer.
6. The television was watching the woman.
7. The grass cut an old man.
8. Some crisps ate the children.

Practise your punctuation

Rewrite these sentences correctly.
Remember the capital letters and full stops.

1. bones eating my likes dog
2. sky blue the is
3. cream I ice like
4. to it rain began
5. the going park we to are

Sometimes a sentence ends with an **exclamation mark** instead of a full stop.

> I really hate winter!

> What a lovely present!

> Stop pinching me!

It can show that we feel strongly about something.

It can show that we are surprised about something.

It is used to give a command.

Practice

Copy the sentences that end with exclamation marks.

What is for dinner?

This tastes delicious!

What a sensible child you are!

Be quiet!

Put down that cat at once!

May I come with you?

Making sure

Copy and punctuate these sentences correctly.
(There are four that need exclamation marks.)

I don't believe it

I'm six years old now

How tall you are

Stop that this minute

What time is it

I really love reading

I walked to school

Practise your punctuation

Punctuate these sentences correctly.

1. the dragon chased the prince
2. has anyone seen my ruler
3. it's not fair
4. my book is on the table
5. thank goodness you've come
6. where is your house

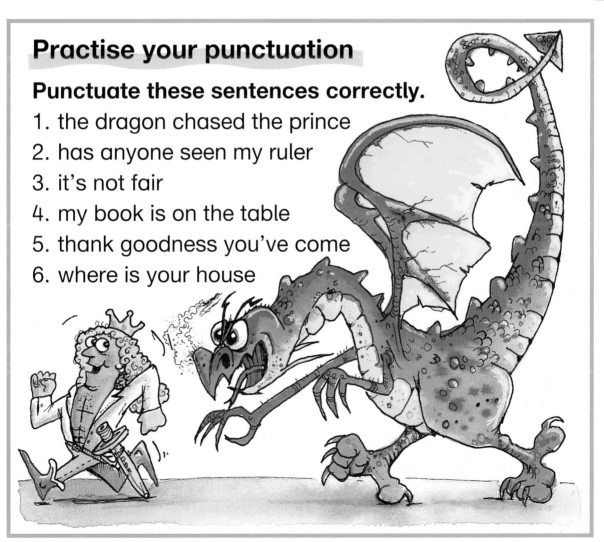

Speech Marks

Speech marks and **speech bubbles** show someone is speaking.

> I like to watch television in the evenings.

Mr Samir said, "I like to watch television in the evening."

We write what the person says inside the speech marks.

Practice

> I will put away the books.

> I will tidy up the cupboard.

> I will clean the brushes.

> I will feed the rabbit.

AHMED

BAMI

LUCY

JAMES

Write what each child said.

1. Ahmed said, "_____."
2. Bami said, "_____."
3. "_____," said James.
4. "_____," said Lucy.

Making sure

**Make up a sensible answer
to write these conversations.**

1. "Where is my tee shirt?"
   Sophie asked.
   "_____," her mum answered.
2. "What would you like for your birthday?"
   Mrs Jenkins asked.
   "_____," replied John.
3. "Why have you got an umbrella?" the man asked.
   "_____," the woman said.
4. The driver asked, "How do I get to the High Street?"
   The girl said, "_____."

Practise your punctuation

**Copy these sentences. Put in the missing
speech marks.**

1. Can you come out to play? Colin asked.
2. I cannot find my tie anywhere! Mr Bentall shouted.
4. Your tea is on the table, Mrs Carter said to her son.
5. What a horrible day! exclaimed Mr Shah.

UNIT 10

Matching Verbs with Nouns

A sentence must make sense.
The **verb** must match with the **noun**.

The dog eat his dinner. ✗

The noun and the verb do not match.

The dog eats his dinner. ✓

The noun and the verb do match.

Practice

Copy these sentences.
Choose a verb from the box to fill in each gap.

roars	bray	hiss	moo	trumpets	neigh

1. Cows _____
2. Donkeys _____
3. Horses _____
4. A lion _____
5. Snakes _____
6. An elephant _____

Making sure

**In each sentence the underlined
verb is wrong.
Write each sentence correctly.**

1. The bells <u>is</u> ringing.
2. There <u>are</u> an apple in
   my bag.
3. Every day I <u>walks</u> to
   school.
4. The clock <u>tick</u> loudly.
5. Aeroplanes <u>lands</u> on
   the runway.
6. I <u>draws</u> with a pencil.
7. A bird <u>are</u> singing in
   the tree.
8. The children <u>is</u> running.

Practise your punctuation

**Match up the beginning and ending of
each sentence.
Write the sentences correctly in your book.**

1. A rocket is   a new pair of trainers.
2. The monster   get out of bed.
3. In the morning I   made of metal.
4. My cat   ride a bike.
5. I can   scares me.
6. I need   chases birds.

More about Verbs (past tense)

Sometimes **verbs** are written in the **past tense**. They tell us what happened some time ago.

Last week Sita visited a museum.

The **verb** is in the **past tense** because it happened some time ago.

Practice

Copy these sentences.
Choose the correct verb to go in each gap.

travelled	took	saw	walked	felt	went

1. On Monday Sita _____ to school with Ben.
2. She _____ a packed lunch with her.
3. The class _____ on a trip.
4. The children _____ to the museum on a coach.
5. They _____ lots of interesting things.
6. Afterwards, Sita _____ very tired.

Making sure

Copy this story.
Try to think of a
suitable verb to
fill each gap.

Yesterday Hari and Lucy _____ for a walk in the
woods. They _____ a noise. They _____ up
and _____ a squirrel in a tree. Nearby some rabbits
_____ playing on the grass. The birds _____ loudly
all around them. In the afternoon, Hari and Lucy
_____ a picnic. On the way home, they saw an owl.
It _____ down to catch a mouse.

Practise your punctuation

In the sentences the underlined verbs are wrong.
Copy the sentences.
Correct the verbs and put in the missing
punctuation marks.

1. on monday I <u>runned</u> in a race.
2. yesterday tom <u>done</u> four pages of writing
3. wesley <u>catched</u> the ball easily
4. last night everyone <u>go</u> to bed early
5. when the man <u>ringed</u> the bell, the dog barked loudly
6. after emma <u>finish</u> her tea she played in the garden

UNIT 12 Commas

A **comma** tells you to **pause**.
Commas are used to separate things in a list.

Practice

Copy these lists. Put in the missing commas.

1. penguins emus ostriches lions elephants
2. red blue orange yellow green
3. a cat a dog two rabbits five mice two hamsters
4. curry spaghetti sausages pizza hamburgers
5. guitar drums trumpet piano tambourine

Making sure

1. Make up some lists of at least five items:
   a) Things you like to eat.
   b) Things you can buy at a bakers.
   c) The names of some friends.
   d) Favourite toys.

2. Write a list of the things which belong to each person below. Do it like this:

A gardener needs a fork, a spade, a hoe and a lawnmower.

A doctor needs

 bandages  a thermometer

a stethoscope medicine

A diver needs

  goggles  a wet suit

flippers  a snorkel

Practise your punctuation

Copy these sentences.
Put in the missing punctuation marks.

1. in his bag carlo has some sandwiches some crisps a packet of biscuits and an apple
2. out of the window maureen could see two cars a lorry a bus and a bicycle
3. the first months of the year are january february march and april
4. my birthday presents were a ball a book a game and a watch

UNIT 13 More Questions

We ask **questions** for lots of reasons.

Whenever you write a sentence that is a **question** you must put:
- a **capital letter** at the beginning
- a **question mark** at the end.

Practice

Match the question to the correct answer.
Then write them out correctly, like this:

1. What colour is the sun? It is yellow.

Questions	Answers
1. What colour is the sun?	I like orange juice best.
2. When is your birthday?	It is in June.
3. Where is London?	I am happy because it is my birthday.
4. What is your favourite drink?	It is yellow.
5. Why are you so happy?	London is in England.

Making sure

Make these sentences into questions.
The first one has been done for you.

1. The window got broken.
   How did the window get broken?
2. The pencil is blunt.
3. Someone is at the door.
4. Tom's birthday was in March.
5. Paris is in France.
6. The cat was stuck up the tree.
7. It will soon be time for lunch.

Practise your punctuation

Copy these sentences. Punctuate them correctly.

1. the racing car was red
2. edinburgh is in scotland
3. in the morning the dragon came back
4. the meal cost five pounds
5. Mrs Martin looked out of the window

Now turn each sentence into a question and
write it down.

Progress Unit

1. Punctuate these sentences correctly.

   a) parrots are colourful birds

   b) a lion can run fast

   c) does a giraffe have a long neck

   d) how many legs has an octopus

   e) crocodiles like to sleep in the sun

2. These stepping stones have **nouns** and **verbs** on them.

tree · eats · girl · climbs · shop · talks · house · crocodile · sits · swims · hops · robot

Write all the **nouns** in a list in your book. Then write all the **verbs** in a list.

3. Write this list of nouns in your book.
   Put in capital letters where they are needed.
   a) april   b) girl   c) apple   d) london
   e) cardiff   f) wednesday   g) garden   h) river
   i) queen ann street   j) forest   k) november
   l) boy   m) monday   n) bird   o) pennington road

4. Join these pairs of sentences
   together to make them into
   one sentence.

   a) Sharks have sharp teeth.
      They live in the sea.
   b) You write with a pencil. You paint with a brush.
   c) We came indoors. It started raining.
   d) The children shouted. They were in the playground.

5. Put these words in the **correct order** to make sentences.
   Punctuate the sentences correctly.
   a) black are some cats
   b) in fly aeroplanes sky the
   c) swim can in sea you day on the sunny a
   d) for we spain holiday went to our

6. Write these sentences. Put in a full stop, question mark
   or exclamation mark where they belong.
   a) How far is it to the beach
   b) What a lovely surprise to see you again
   c) Put the box on the floor
   d) Look out There's a monster behind you

7. Copy these sentences and put in the missing **speech marks**.

a) Where are you going? Mark asked his mum.

b) I'm going to the shops, his mum replied.

c) May I come? Mark said.

d) Yes you may but hurry up, his mum called.

8. The underlined **verbs** are wrong.
Write each sentence again correctly.

a) A kangaroo <u>hop</u> but snakes slide.

b) Where <u>is</u> you going?

c) Every day I <u>wakes</u> up early.

d) The gardener <u>are</u>
digging up the weeds.

9. Copy these sentences.
Fill in the gaps with sensible **verbs**.

a) Yesterday I _____ in the sea. It _____ very cold.

b) Last week the greedy boy _____ twelve bananas.

c) Last night the wind _____ down a tree.

d) It _____ on the way home and Tom _____ wet.

10. Punctuate these sentences correctly
and write them in your book.

a) my favourite colours are red blue green and yellow

b) is art maths spelling or science your best lesson

c) when I come I will bring a bat a ball some
swimming trunks and a towel

d) amber's birthday is either on monday tuesday
wednesday or thursday